Contents • Inhalt • Table des Matières

1. Le petit nègre   2

2. Arabesque No. 1   4

3. Élégie   10

4. Petite pièce   12

5. Danse Bohémienne   14

6. La plus que lente   18

7. The Little Shepherd   24

8. Jimbo's Lullaby   26

9. La fille aux cheveux de lin   30

10. Golliwogg's Cake Walk   32

Preface

The clarinet has featured greatly in the orchestral works of Claude Debussy as its wealth of tonal colour is perfectly suited to his impressionistic compositional style. However, Debussy wrote very few solo works for the instrument. The *Première Rhapsodie pour clarinette et orchestre* is his only major composition in this genre. There is also his *Petite pièce pour clarinette et piano* which I have included in this publication which was originally composed as a sight reading test for the *Conservatoire de Paris*, although it is far more significant than most pieces used for this purpose.

This album has been arranged with the aim of providing clarinettists with popular performance material written by this great composer. The pieces are all of moderate length and are suitable for players of moderate to advanced technical skills.

April 2004   James Rae

Vorwort

Die Klarinette taucht in Claude Debussys Orchesterwerken häufig auf, da sich ihr Klangfarbenreichtum hervorragend für seinen impressionistischen Kompositionsstil eignet. Debussy schrieb allerdings nur wenige Solowerke für das Instrument. Die *Première Rhapsodie pour clarinette et orchestre* ist seine einzige große Komposition in diesem Genre. Darüber hinaus gibt es noch das *Petite pièce pour clarinette et piano*, welches ich in diese Ausgabe mit aufgenommen habe. Dieses Stück wurde ursprünglich als Blattspieltest für das *Conservatoire de Paris* komponiert, auch wenn es weit anspruchsvoller ist als die meisten für solch einen Zweck eingesetzten Stücke.

Die Zusammenstellung dieses Albums verfolgte das Ziel, Klarinettisten beliebte Konzertstücke dieses großen Komponisten zur Verfügung zu stellen. Alle Stücke sind mäßig lang und für Interpreten der Mittelstufe sowie für fortgeschrittene Spieler geeignet.

April 2004   James Rae

Préface

La clarinette apparaît fréquemment dans les œuvres pour orchestre de Claude Debussy, la richesse de son timbre se prêtant à son style de composition impressionniste. Debussy n'écrivit pourtant que peu d'œuvres solistes pour cet instrument. La *Première Rhapsodie pour clarinette et orchestre* est sa seule grande composition dans ce genre. N'oublions pas par ailleurs la *Petite Pièce pour clarinette et piano* que j'ai intégrée dans cette édition. Cette pièce fut composée à l'origine comme morceau à vue pour le *Conservatoire de Paris*, même si elle est beaucoup plus ambitieuse que la plupart des pièces conçues pour un tel objectif.

En organisant cet album, nous nous sommes donné pour objectif de mettre à la disposition des clarinettistes les pièces de concert favorites de ce grand compositeur. Toutes les pièces sont d'un longeur moyen et adaptées aux interprètes de niveau moyen ainsi qu'à ceux de niveau avancé.

Avril 2004   James Rae

Claude Debussy

Clarinet Album

Arranged for B♭ Clarinet and Piano

by **JAMES RAE**

www.universaledition.com
vienna · london · new york

UE 21 264
ISMN 979-0-008-07548-3
UPC 8-03452-02280-0
ISBN 978-3-7024-2739-9

1. Le petit nègre

Clarinet in B♭

Claude Debussy
(1862–1918)
arr. James Rae

Universal Edition UE 21 264a

2. Arabesque No. 1

4

3. Élégie

4. Petite pièce

5. Danse Bohémienne

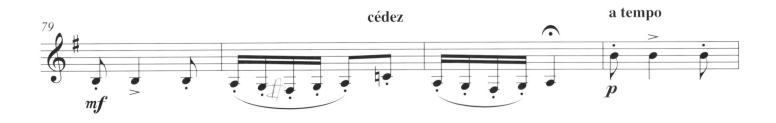

6. La plus que lente

12

7. The Little Shepherd

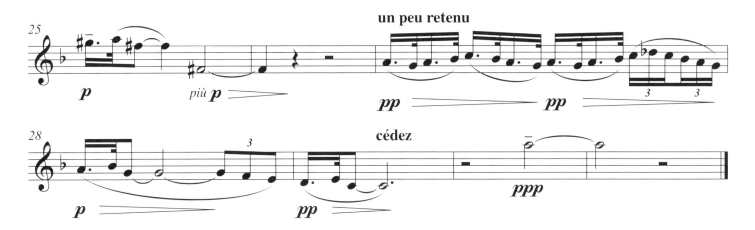

8. Jimbo's Lullaby

16

9. La fille aux cheveux de lin

Très calme et doucement expressif ($\bullet = 66$)

10. Golliwogg's Cake Walk

1. Le petit nègre

Claude Debussy
(1862–1918)
arr. James Rae

Universal Edition UE 21 264

UE 21 264

2. Arabesque No. 1

3. Élégie

11

4. Petite pièce

Modéré et doucement rythmé

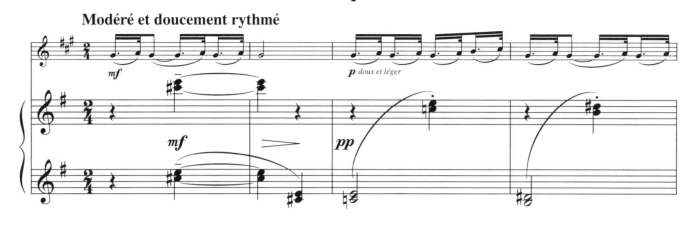

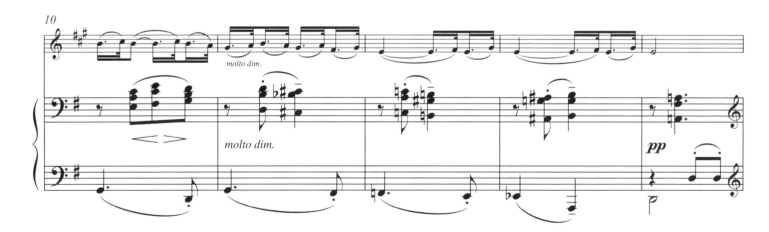

13

5. Danse Bohémienne

6. La plus que lente

19

20

21

23

7. The Little Shepherd

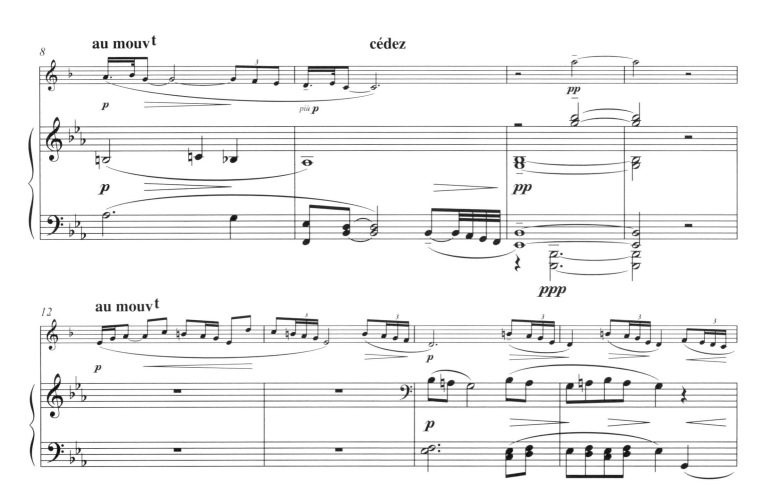

8. Jimbo's Lullaby

9. La fille aux cheveux de lin

10. Golliwogg's Cake Walk

34

un peu moins vite

cédez   a tempo

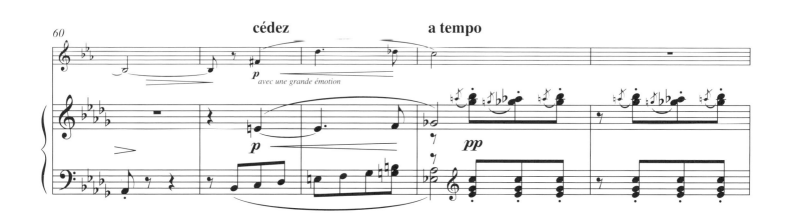

35

UE 21 264

World Music

Ensemble Instrumentation:
Melody I / II in C (Flute, Violin)
Melody I / II in B♭ (Clarinet, Saxophone)
Guitar / Accordion
Piano
Bass
Percussion

Scotland
*Scotland the Brave, My
Love is like a Red, Red Rose,
The Skye Boat Song, Mhairi's
Wedding, 100 Pipers*

(James Rae) [2]
Ensemble + CD
UE 31525

Israel
*Tchiribim Tchiribom, Shalosh
bnot hapele, Dror Yikra,
Ahavat Hadassa, Hava Nagila*

(Timna Brauer/Elias Meiri) [2]
Ensemble + CD
UE 31523
Play-Along Clarinet + CD
UE 31555

Russia
*Kalinka, Schwarze Augen,
Der Mond scheint, Steppe
rund herum, Valenky*

(Iwan Malachowskij) [2]
Ensemble + CD
UE 31524
Play-Along Clarinet + CD
UE 31557

Brazil
*Choro da Luz, Maracatu,
Cantigas de Roda,
Quebrasamba, Coco*

(Jovino Santos Neto) [2-3]
Ensemble + CD
UE 31526
Play-Along Clarinet + CD
UE 31562

Argentina
*Tango, Vals Criollo, Milonga,
Chacarera, Zamba*

(Diego Collatti) [2-3]
Ensemble + CD
UE 31528
Play-Along Clarinet + CD
UE 31566

Klezmer
*The Silver Crown, Ma Yofes,
Romanian Hora, Stoliner Nign,
Dorohoi Khusidl*

(Yale Strom) [2-3]
Ensemble + CD
UE 31529
Play-Along Clarinet + CD
UE 31569

Cuba
*Bolero, Mambo, Cha Cha, Son
Montuno, Rumba*

(Richard Graf/Richard Filz) [2]
Ensemble + CD
UE 31521